Andrew Brodie Basics

LET'S DO SPELLING

FOR AGES 10-11

with over **100** reward stickers

- Over 400 words to practise and learn
- Regular progress tests
- Extra tips and brain booster questions

Published 2014 by Bloomsbury Publishing Plc
50 Bedford Square, London, WC1B 3DP

www.bloomsbury.com

ISBN 978-1-4729-0863-6

Copyright © 2014 Bloomsbury Publishing
Text copyright © 2014 Andrew Brodie
Cover and inside illustrations of Comma the Cat and Andrew Brodie © 2014 Nikalas Catlow
Other inside illustrations © 2014 Steve Evans

A CIP catalogue for this book is available from the British Library.

10 9 8 7 6 5 4 3 2 1

Printed in China by Leo Paper Products

This book is produced using paper that is made from wood grown in managed, sustainable forests. It is natural, renewable and recyclable. The logging and manufacturing process conform to the environmental regulations of the country of origin.

To see our full range of titles visit **www.bloomsbury.com**

BLOOMSBURY

Notes for parents

What's in this book

This is the sixth book in an exciting new series of *Andrew Brodie Basics: Let's Do Spelling*. Each book contains more than four hundred words especially chosen to boost children's confidence in spelling and to reflect the demands of the new National Curriculum.

By the end of Key Stage 2, most children are confident in the skills of 'segmenting' (breaking words down to spell them) and 'blending' (combining sounds together to read whole words) and will apply these skills when learning the spellings in this book. Of course, some words do not follow regular phonic patterns so your child will need to learn these 'tricky' words by looking at individual letters and the general shape of the word.

How you can help

To get the most out of this book, take the time to discuss the activities with your child when there are no distractions around and they are in a responsive and enthusiastic mood. Talk through each of the practice words and what they mean by using them in spoken sentences, or by asking your child to make up sentences containing the words. Putting up posters of useful words around the house, such as the days of the week and the months of the year, might also help with spelling generally.

To begin with, your child might find the spellings in this book quite tricky, but as they work their way through the activities and become familiar with the spelling patterns their confidence should grow. The level of difficulty is increased gradually throughout the book, but some spelling patterns are repeated to provide lots of opportunities for reinforcement and practice. Always be ready to provide plenty of encouragement and explain that they should learn from their mistakes rather than get disheartened.

Look out for...

Look, cover, write, check

Some pages feature 'Look, cover, write, check' exercises. Your child might have already come across this strategy in school. Ask your child to **look** carefully at each word, learning the shape of it and any letter patterns it contains. When they feel they know it, ask them to **cover** it with their hand or a piece of paper and to try writing it. They then look back at the original word and **write** it again to **check** that they really know it.

Comma the Cat

Look out for Comma the Cat who tells your child which words to focus on for the progress test at the end of each section. You could help your child to learn these words by posting them around the house on sticky notes or writing them on flashcards for quick memory games.

Brodie's Brain Boosters

Brodie's Brain Boosters feature quick extra activities designed to make your child think, using the skills and knowledge they already have. Some of these will ask your child to think of rhyming words. Don't worry if your child finds a rhyming word that doesn't match the spelling pattern of the given word. Use the opportunity to compare the spellings – looking carefully at words is, of course, the whole point of the activity!

The answer section

The answer section at the end of this book can also be a useful learning tool. Ask your child to compare their spellings with the correct spellings provided on the answer pages. If they have spelt the words correctly, congratulate them, but if they haven't, don't let them worry about it! Instead, encourage them to learn the correct versions. Give lots of praise for any success.

Word Endings

Change these ant words into ance words. The first one has been done for you.

distant ➡ **distance**

assistant ➡

important ➡

Change these ent words into ence words.

different ➡

absent ➡

silent ➡

independent ➡

confident ➡

insistent ➡

evident ➡

Choose words from above to complete the sentences below.

There was an absence of ———————— at the crime scene.

Do you know the ———————— between practice and practise?

The magician's ———————— was very brave.

Mum told me I need to be more ————————.

I gain more ———————— when I practise my spellings.

The headteacher stressed the ———————— of Year 6.

I prefer sprinting to long ———————— running.

Comma says...

Learn these words for your first progress test.

assistance

evidence   **importance**

independent

Brodie's Brain Booster

Can you think of any other words ending in 'ance'?

Practise the Words

The prefixes mono and uni are both related to '1'.

LOOK (THEN COVER)	WRITE	CHECK
monopoly		
monopolise		
monologue		
monorail		
unicorn		
unicycle		
union		
unity		
united		
reunion		

Choose words from above to complete the sentences below. Remember to use capital letters if they are needed.

England, Northern Ireland, Scotland and Wales are all countries in the _____ Kingdom.

Some people _____ the conversation so you can't get a word in!

Rugby _____ is an important sport in this country.

Most people in my family like playing the game called _____.

The clown rode round the ring on a _____.

'We must work together in _____!' said the Prime Minister.

Comma says...

Learn these words for your first progress test.

monorail   unicycle

reunion   monologue

4

Number Words

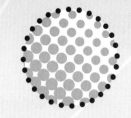

Sort the words into 'number' groups.

triangular   nonagon   pentagon   triplets   quintuplet   ~~biceps~~

centenary   ~~bicentenary~~   quadruped   decagon   ~~biplane~~   heptagon   quartet

pentathlon   tricycle   century   hexagonal   decathlon   quintet

quadrilateral   centigrade   octagonal

Copy the words on to the correct list. One group has been done for you.

2
biceps
bicentenary
biplane

5

3

6

7

4

8

9

10

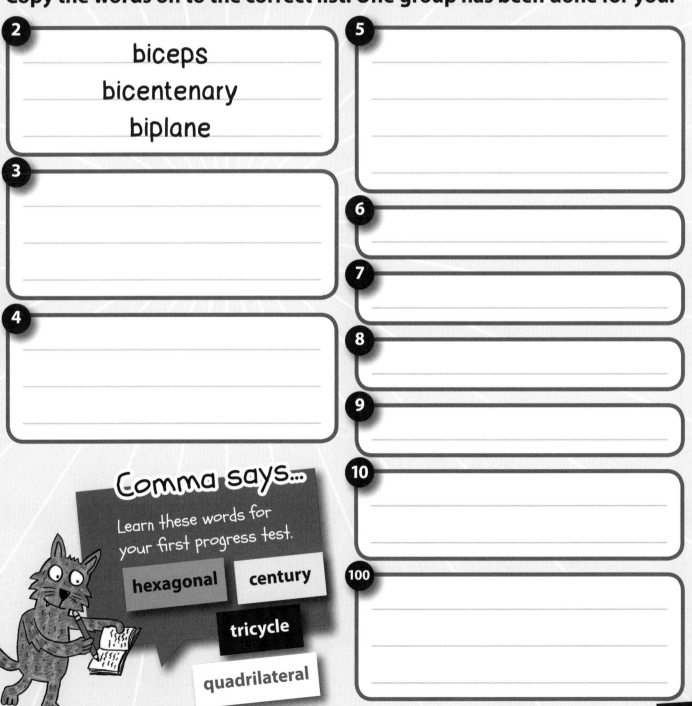

Comma says...

Learn these words for your first progress test.

hexagonal   century

tricycle

quadrilateral

100

5

Sort the Words

Some words start with the same or similar prefix.

aerodynamic   hydraulic   audience   auditorium   hydrogen   aeroplane

audio   subject   subconscious   aquarium   hydroelectric   photocopier

submarine   photographic   audible   submerge   audition   subheading

aquatic   aerial

Sort the words into prefix families.

Words starting with aqua

Words starting with audio or similar

Words starting with hydro or hydra

Words starting with photo

Words starting with aero or similar

Words starting with sub

Comma says...

Learn these words for your first progress test.

aquarium   aeroplane

audition   submarine

Brodie's Brain Booster

Use a dictionary to find out what each prefix means.

Practise the Words

Cover each word and see if you can write it without looking. Then check and write it again.

LOOK (THEN COVER)	WRITE	CHECK
disguise		
biscuit		
guidance		
guitars		
guitarist		
catalogue		
rogue		
guarantee		
language		
linguist		

Choose words from above to complete the sentences below.

We had a look through the _____ to choose a new coat.

Most _____ have six strings.

The _____ was a great musician.

I would like to learn a _____ such as French or German.

Brodie's Brain Booster
Can you think of a word that rhymes with royal?

Comma says...
Learn these words for your first progress test.

guidance   catalogue

disguise   guarantee

Use the words you have been practising to fill the gaps.

1   The police were searching for _____.

2   The _____ circled the runway before landing.

3   I went to the party wearing a _____.

4   The garden was _____ because it had six sides.

5   The new computer has a three-year _____.

6   Do you realise the _____ of the situation?

7   I had an _____ for the main part in the play.

8   They asked me to perform a _____.

9   There were lots of different clothes in the _____.

10 There were hundreds of fish in the _____.

11 'Can I be of any _____?' asked the shopkeeper.

12 'Yes, please, I need some _____ with how to fit the memory card,' replied the shopper.

13 A parallelogram is a type of _____.

14 The toddler was riding on a red _____.

15 It must be very difficult to ride on a _____.

16 All the school friends met up for a _____.

17 The _____ dived under the surface of the sea.

18 People have travelled more and more over the last _____.

19 We saw the sites when we travelled on the _____.

20 Some people like to be _____ and do things on their own.

Score _____ /20

Sort the Words

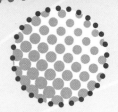

Some words are related to each other because they have similar parts or similar meanings.

hesitantly • observe • tolerant • substantially • hesitation • expectantly • observation • substance • substantial • expectant • frequency • tolerance • frequently • expectation • hesitant • toleration • confident • observant • confidence • frequent • confidential

Sort the words into groups. The first group has been done for you.

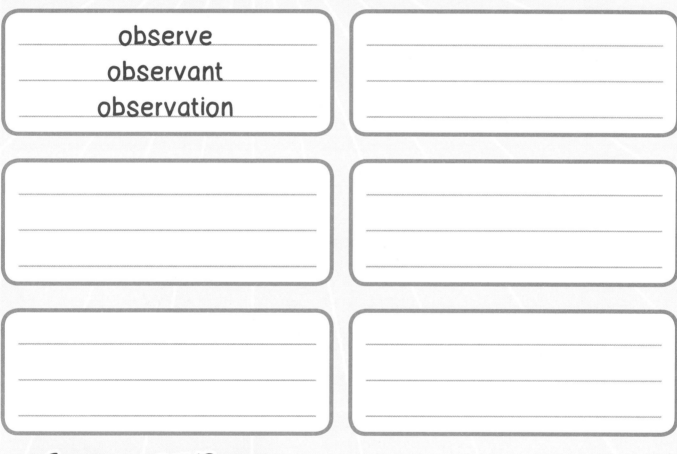

observe
observant
observation

Practise the Words

Cover each word and see if you can write it without looking.
Then check and write it again.

LOOK (THEN COVER)	WRITE	CHECK
accommodation		
bruise		
category		
definite		
embarrass		
foreign		
government		
hindrance		
immediately		
lightning		

Choose words from above to complete the sentences below.

After I fell over, a big _____ came up on my leg.

'Come here _____!' the woman shouted to her dog.

'Are you _____ that your answer is correct?' asked the teacher.

The _____ decides the laws for the country.

Comma says...

Learn these words for your second progress test.

accommodation   government

immediately   definite

Brodie's Brain Booster

Can you think of a word that rhymes with 'bruise'?

Sort the Words

Read the words below. Some words include qua and some include que.

grotesque   queue   quantity   disqualify   qualifying   quality

qualified   quarrelled   qualify   sequence   quarrelling   antique

conquer   qualification   oblique   cheque   quarrel   equator

earthquake   mosque

Copy the words on to the correct list.

WORDS WITH qua

_____

_____

_____

_____

_____

_____

_____

_____

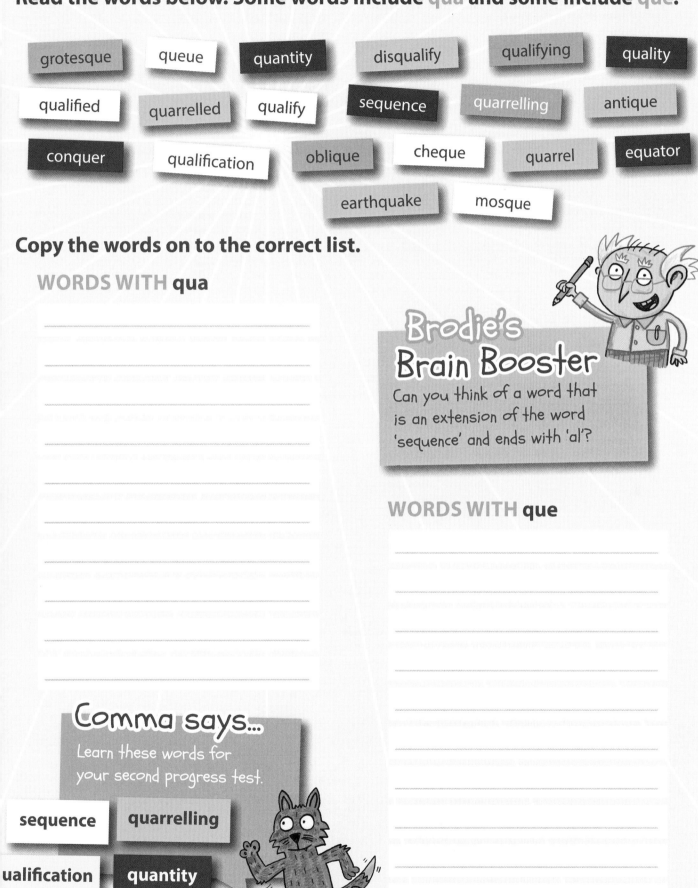

Brodie's Brain Booster

Can you think of a word that is an extension of the word 'sequence' and ends with 'al'?

WORDS WITH que

_____

_____

_____

_____

_____

_____

_____

Comma says...

Learn these words for your second progress test.

sequence   quarrelling

ualification   quantity

Alphabetical Order

Read the words below. Sometimes you need to look at the second, third or further letters of a word to work out alphabetical order.

profit knight obedient applicable practice solemn

continue adorably prophet obedience stationary duplicate

stationery practise borough conversation applicably bough consumer

plough application duet container temperature knife thorough

Write the words in alphabetical order.

Comma says...

Learn these words for your second progress test.

stationary practice

stationery practise

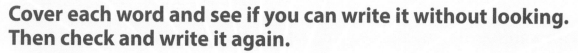

Write the Words

Cover each word and see if you can write it without looking.
Then check and write it again.

LOOK (THEN COVER)	WRITE	CHECK
however	....	....
therefore	....	....
photograph	....	....
autograph	....	....
microscope	....	....
microphone	....	....
supersonic	....	....
superior	....	....
superimpose	....	....
subtle	....	....

Choose words from above to complete the sentences below.

I looked absolutely terrible in the school _____.

I asked the celebrity for her _____.

I wanted to be early. _____, I hadn't accounted for the traffic.

The aeroplane was travelling at _____ speeds.

I looked through the _____ at the butterfly's wing.

Comma says...
Learn these words for
your second progress test.

microscopic   **photographic**

supersonic   **superior**

Brodie's Brain Booster
Can you think of a word
that ends with 'ever'?

Use the words you have been practising to fill the gaps.

1   'Make a very careful _____ of the plant,' said the science teacher.

2   The plane was travelling at _____ speeds.

3   We had great _____ at a really nice hotel.

4   I travel to London quite _____ .

5   I bought a ruler, some pencils, a writing pad and other _____ equipment.

6   Germs are so tiny, they are _____ .

7   As soon as we heard the fire alarm the teacher said, 'leave the classroom _____ !'

8   There was a long queue of _____ vehicles.

9   We should try to be _____ of other people.

10 'Stop _____ !' Mum said to the children when they were arguing.

11 The boy had a _____ memory for numbers.

12 The cat looked at its owner _____ when she opened the fridge.

13 The coach had a special _____ for teaching gymnastics.

14 The numbers were arranged in a _____ of multiples of three.

15 The doctor's _____ has lots of patients.

16 We need to _____ the multiplication tables.

17 'This model is _____ to that one,' said the salesperson.

18 There is a large _____ of books in the library.

19 'Are you _____ about the result?'

20 Lots of people work for the _____ .

Score   /20

Sort the Words

Dogs and cats have four legs but we are NOT related!

Some words are **related** to each other because they have similar parts or similar meanings.

preparing   ~~definite~~   infinity   preparation   redefine   definition

prepared   ~~excluding~~   define   exclude   exclusive   excluded   finite

definitely   unprepared   prepare   exclusion   infinite   exclusively   infinitely

Copy the words on to the correct list.

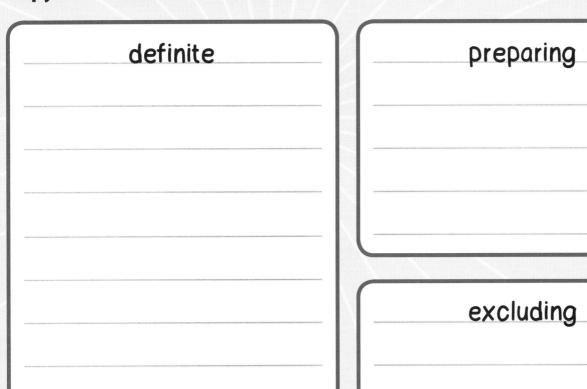

definite

preparing

excluding

Comma says...

Learn these words for your third progress test.

definition   infinity   preparation   exclusively

Practise the Words

Cover each word and see if you can write it without looking.
Then check and write it again.

LOOK (THEN COVER)	WRITE	CHECK
precarious		
previous		
according		
achieve		
twelfth		
variety		
rhyme		
rhythm		
occupy		
occur		

Choose words from above to complete the sentences below.

My birthday is on the _____ of January.

Solar eclipses do not _____ very often.

The climber was balanced on the cliff in a very _____ position.

I would like to _____ high scores in my tests.

Brodie's Brain Booster

Can you think of a word that can be made by adding a suffix to the word 'rhythm'?

Comma says...
Learn these words for your third progress test.

achievement   occupation

variety   previous

16

Pair the Words

Read the words below and then join each one to its pair.
The first one has been done for you.

royal	horizontal
actual	generally
general	originally
eventual	angelic
industry	royalty
rehearse	industrial
horizon	eventually
vertical	actually
original	vertically
angel	rehearsal

Comma says...

Learn these words for your third progress test.

actually **originally**

eventually **rehearsal**

Brodie's Brain Booster

Can you think of an extended version of 'cruel'?

Alphabetical Order

Read the words below. Sometimes you need to look at the second, third or further letters of a word to work out alphabetical order.

apparent whoever explanation amateur whenever existence although excellent primarily portable exaggerate controversy whatever conscious aggressive yacht meanwhile ancient portfolio prescription wherever vehicle primary conscience convenience vegetable

Write the words in alphabetical order.

_____ _____ _____

_____ _____ _____

_____ _____ _____

_____ _____ _____

_____ _____ _____

_____ _____ _____

Comma says...

Learn these words for your third progress test.

aggressive

explanation

conscience

yacht

Write the Words

Cover each word and see if you can write it without looking.
Then check and write it again.

LOOK (THEN COVER)	WRITE	CHECK
appreciate		
attached		
available		
average		
awkward		
sufficient		
suggest		
symbol		
system		
February		
secondary		
estuary		
temporary		
temporarily		
diesel		
petrol		
frequent		
frequently		
frequency		
squeal		

Brodie's Brain Booster

Use these letters to make one word:
n e c t o n i n t
Clue: Europe, Africa and Asia are all one of these.

Comma says...

Learn these words for your third progress test.

available secondary sufficient temporary

Use the words you have been practising to fill the gaps.

1 After primary school, people move on to _____ school.

2 The books could be bought _____ online.

3 Some other books are _____ from lots of shops.

4 Climbing a mountain is a great _____ .

5 What _____ would you like to have when you grow up?

6 The dog was growling loudly and looked very _____ .

7 A large _____ was moored in the marina.

8 It's impossible to count to _____ .

9 I had a guilty _____ after eating the very last chocolate.

10 After a lot of _____ we were ready to go.

11 Are these traffic lights permanent or _____ ?

12 'Can you give me an _____ of long division?' asked the boy.

13 I like a _____ of different chocolates.

14 We went for a _____ of the school play.

15 My _____ school was in the countryside.

16 '_____ I came from Scotland, but now I live in England,' said the man.

17 'Can you give me the _____ of the word 'efficient'?' asked the teacher.

18 I'd like to buy a new phone but I don't have _____ money.

19 I can keep saving up so that _____ I'll have enough.

20 _____ , I'm not sure I want a new phone.

Score ____ / 20

Sort the Words

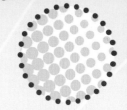

Some words are made by adding suffixes or prefixes to a root word.

qualifying commercial qualification disqualified qualified

finance disrespect commerce financier disrespectful disqualification

commercialise financial qualify respectful disqualifying qualify

disqualify commercialisation finances respect

Copy the words on to the correct list.

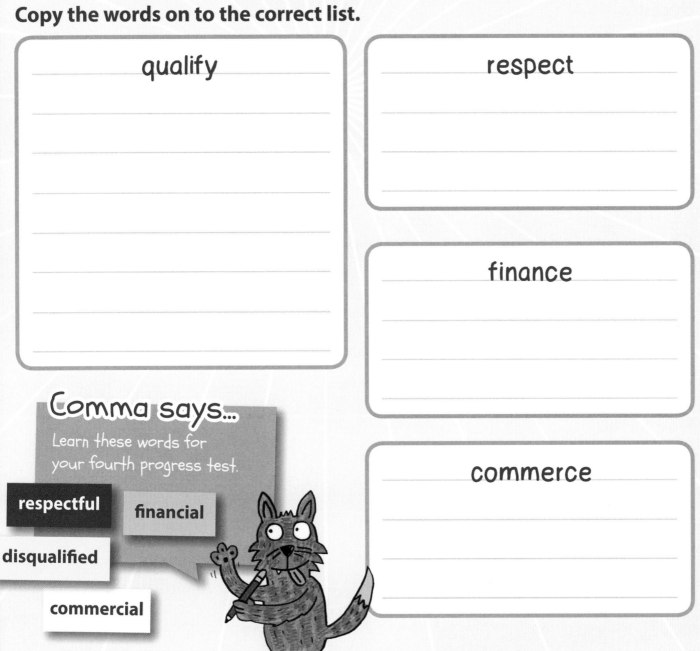

qualify	respect

finance

commerce

Comma says...

Learn these words for your fourth progress test.

respectful **financial**

disqualified

commercial

Tricky Words

Cover each word and see if you can write it without looking.
Then check and write it again.

LOOK (THEN COVER)	WRITE	CHECK
initial		
initially		
cooperate		
deceive		
deceitful		
receive		
receipt		
reception		
ceiling		
perception		

Choose words from above to complete the sentences below.

We should not tell lies and _____ people.

People who tell lies are _____.

My sister is in the _____ class.

I found the _____ lesson quite hard but, after that, all the others seemed easy.

Brodie's Brain Booster

Can you change the word 'cooperate' by adding a suffix or prefix to it?

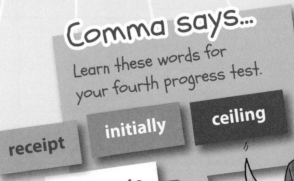

Comma says...

Learn these words for your fourth progress test.

receipt   initially   ceiling

cooperate

Pair the Words

Read the words below. Sort them into pairs where one word is the root word and the other word is an extended version of the root word. The first pair has been done for you.

contest contemporary consult conscious ~~doubtful~~ contestant autumn

continental consider islander adventurous island temporary consciously

autumnal adventure continent considerable consultation ~~doubt~~

---

doubt
doubtful

Comma says...

Learn these words for your fourth progress test.

islander   considerable

consultation

adventurous

Alphabetical Order

Read the words below. Sometimes you need to look at the second, third or further letters of a word to work out alphabetical order.

complicated identity persuade mineral anxious operation

obstinate ordinary miserable suggestion physical medical surgery

angel surrender community successful prejudice another parliament

medieval angle competition opportunity comprehension immediate

Write the words in alphabetical order.

Comma says...

Learn these words for your fourth progress test.

community

immediate

miserable

ordinary

Write the Words

Always use your best handwriting!

Cover each word and see if you can write it without looking. Then check and write it again.

LOOK (THEN COVER)	WRITE	CHECK
object		
objection		
objectionable		
agree		
agreement		
agreeable		
control		
controlling		
controlled		
controller		
council		
councillor		
cancel		
cancelled		
cancelling		
cancellation		
cruel		
cruelty		
prophecy		
prophesy		

Comma says...

Learn these words for your fourth progress test.

objection

controlling

prophecy

cancelled

Brodie's Brain Booster

Use these letters to make one word:
i g s t r e u n a
Clue: you write this at the end of a letter.

Progress Test 4

Use the words you have been practising to fill the gaps.

1. I made a _____ that I would have a spelling test.

2. Some people like to have _____ holidays where they do lots of exciting and dangerous things.

3. The player was _____ for cheating.

4. The trip had to be _____ because of illness.

5. My mum painted the _____ white so that my room was much brighter.

6. We are in such a hurry we will have to make an _____ departure.

7. Dad said the car dealer wanted a _____ amount of money for the new car.

8. I had difficulty _____ the toy boat.

9. Everyone needs to take part in _____ activities.

10. A person who lives on an island is called an _____.

11. I have no _____ to people singing so long as they don't disturb me.

12. It's much better to be happy than _____.

13. I watched a television _____ about the new computer.

14. Banks can be described as _____ institutions.

15. Young people should be _____ to older people.

16. _____ I expected spelling to be difficult but it's not so bad!

17. 'Would you like the _____ coffee or the special one?' asked the barista.

18. I had a _____ with the doctor.

19. People are more successful when they _____ with each other.

20. The shopkeeper gave me a _____ when I bought the new clothes.

Score _____ / 20

Sort the Words

Dogs **regularly** cause trouble!

Remember that some words are made by adding suffixes or prefixes to a root word.

~~sign~~ ~~peculiar~~ familiar irregular agricultural

popularly ~~popular~~ ~~family~~ regularly peculiarity

familiarity population ~~regular~~ ~~agriculture~~ popularity signature

~~particular~~ peculiarly particularly unfamiliar

popular

family

regular

peculiar

sign

agriculture

particular

Comma says...

Learn these words for your fifth progress test.

agricultural   unfamiliar

popularity

particularly

Practise the Words

Cover each word and see if you can write it without looking.
Then check and write it again.

LOOK (THEN COVER)	WRITE	CHECK
compliment		
complement		
draft		
draught		
principal		
principle		
descent		
dissent		
desert		
dessert		

Choose the singular or plural of the words above to complete the sentences below.

The head of the college is called the _____ .

Everybody should try to follow honest _____ .

Some _____ are very hot in the daytime but very cold at night.

We had fruit salad with ice-cream for _____ .

Comma says...

Learn these words for your fifth progress test.

compliment   **draught**

dessert   **principal**

Brodie's Brain Booster

Can you write an adjective related to the word desert and means that nobody is about?

28

Pair the Words

Read the words below and then join each one to its pair.
The first one has been done for you.

individual	interruption
interfere	mischievous
interrupt	individually
marvel	dependable
mischief	recommendation
recognise	sincerely
recommend	interference
secret	secretary
depend	marvellous
sincere	recognition

Comma says...

Learn these words for your fifth progress test.

interruption   mischievous

recommendation

individually

Brodie's Brain Booster

Can you think of another word that can be made from the root word 'sincere'?

Alphabetical Order

Read the words below. Sometimes you need to look at the second, third or further letters of a word to work out alphabetical order.

atmosphere   privilege   attraction   phenomenon   consequence   shoulder   consistent

tournament   border   tortuous   stomach   profession   attractive

atmospheric   soldier   pronunciation   shattered   conclusion   bought   phenomenal

boarder   tornado   brought   tremendous   programme   considerable

Write the words in alphabetical order.

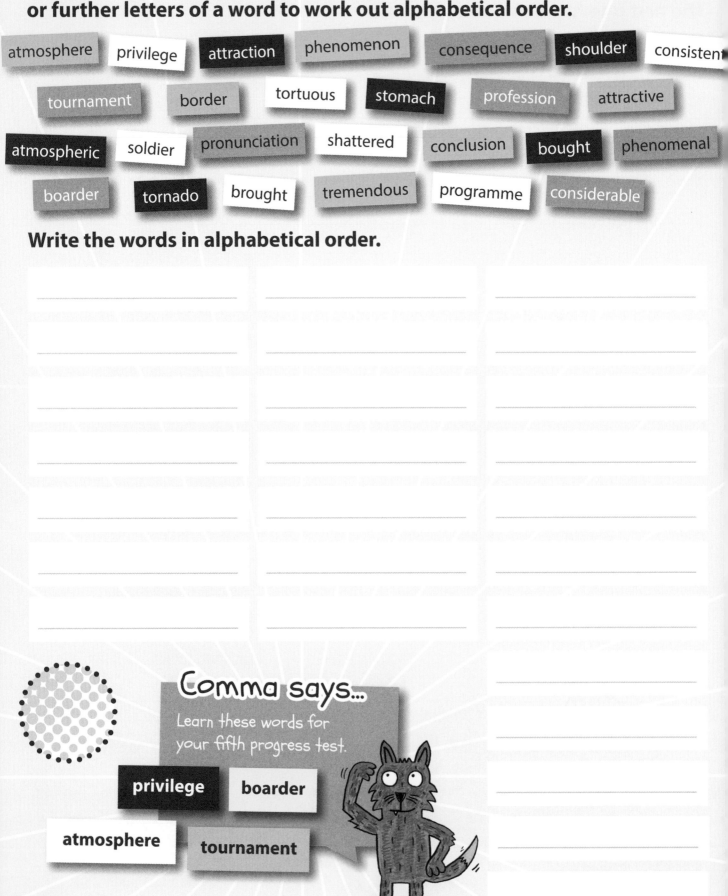

Comma says...

Learn these words for your fifth progress test.

privilege   boarder

atmosphere   tournament

Write the Words

Cover each word and see if you can write it without looking. Then check and write it again.

LOOK (THEN COVER)	WRITE	CHECK
vicious		
viciously		
viciousness		
precious		
preciously		
preciousness		
delight		
delightful		
delicious		
deliciously		
deliciousness		
delicate		
delicacy		
malice		
malicious		
maliciously		
maliciousness		
innocent		
innocently		
innocence		

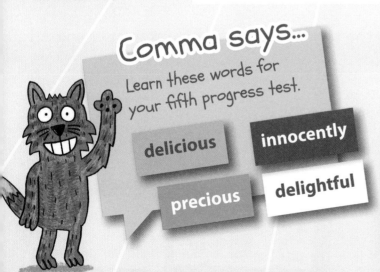

Comma says...

Learn these words for your fifth progress test.

delicious innocently precious delightful

Brodie's Brain Booster

Can you think of a word that rhymes with 'malice'?

31

Use the words you have been practising to fill the gaps.

1 Tractors are very useful _____ machines.

2 The Earth's _____ is a layer of gases that surround our planet.

3 After knocking over the flowerpots, the dog looked _____ at its owner.

4 'That dog is always so _____!' said the owner.

5 'What a _____ picture,' said the teacher when she looked at my drawing.

6 I was very pleased with the _____.

7 After my main course I had a _____.

8 My sticky toffee pudding was _____.

9 The netball _____ took place at the secondary school.

10 My mum doesn't have any _____ jewellery.

11 'I'm sorry for the _____' said the man, as he burst into the room.

12 I am surprised at the _____ of the dancing programme.

13 I knew most of the people at the party but one or two were _____ to me.

14 The long division questions were _____ difficult.

15 Do you have a _____ for a good film I could watch?

16 'It is a great _____ to be speaking to you today,' said the visitor as he started his speech.

17 The boy is a _____ at the school but he goes home at weekends.

18 The college _____ asked the students to work hard.

19 My grandmother said that there was a _____ coming under the door.

20 'I'm going to speak to each of you _____,' said the teacher.

Score _____ /20

Sort the Words

Remember that some words are made by adding suffixes or prefixes to a root word.

changeless   considerably   exchangeable   tolerably

changelessness   exchange   exchangeability   tolerable   enforcement   ~~consider~~

consideration   ~~force~~   considerable   forcible   ~~change~~   ~~tolerate~~

changeability   enforce   toleration   changeable

Can you sort the words into groups?

consider

force

tolerate

change

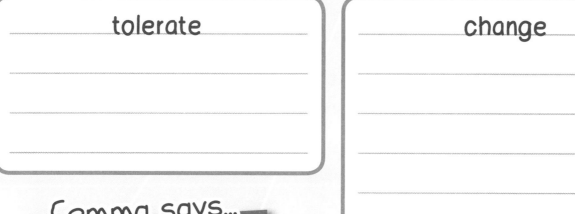

Comma says...

Learn these words for your sixth progress test.

considerably   exchangeable

tolerable   enforce

Practise the Words

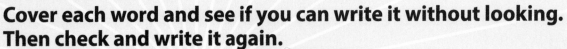

Cover each word and see if you can write it without looking.
Then check and write it again.

LOOK (THEN COVER)	WRITE	CHECK
decent		
decency		
advice		
advise		
device		
devise		
licence		
license		
affect		
effect		

Choose words from above to complete the sentences below.

'Let me give you some _____,' she said.

'I _____ you to sit quietly and get all your work done.'

See if you can _____ a method for finding the volume of the ball.

Do you have a _____ to drive a car?

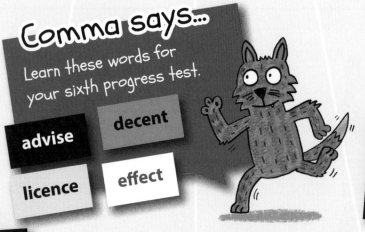

Comma says...
Learn these words for your sixth progress test.

advise   decent   licence   effect

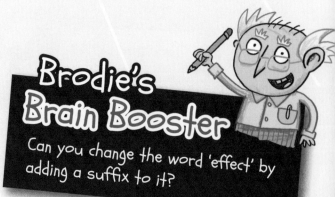

Brodie's Brain Booster
Can you change the word 'effect' by adding a suffix to it?

Tricky Mathematical Words

Some mathematical words are very tricky.

Cover each word and see if you can write it without looking. Then check and write it again.

LOOK (THEN COVER)	WRITE	CHECK
circumference		
parallelogram		
trapezium		
rhombus		
tetrahedron		
dodecahedron		
cylinder		
cylindrical		
equilateral		
isosceles		

Choose words from above to complete the sentences below.

A _____ is a solid shape with twelve faces.

Most food and drink cans are _____ in shape.

A triangle with three equal sides is called an _____ triangle.

We can measure volumes of liquid using a measuring _____.

The perimeter of a circle is called its _____.

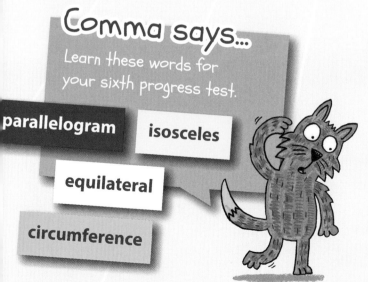

Comma says...

Learn these words for your sixth progress test.

parallelogram

isosceles

equilateral

circumference

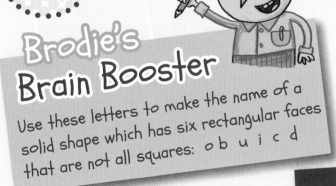

Brodie's Brain Booster

Use these letters to make the name of a solid shape which has six rectangular faces that are not all squares: o b u i c d

Alphabetical Order

Read the words on the list. Sometimes you need to look at the second, third or further letters of a word to work out alphabetical order.

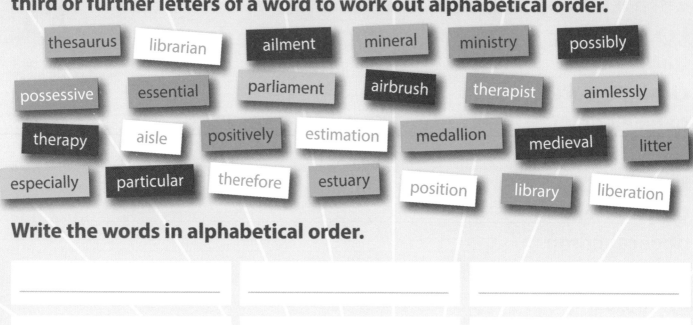

thesaurus librarian ailment mineral ministry possibly

possessive essential parliament airbrush therapist aimlessly

therapy aisle positively estimation medallion medieval litter

especially particular therefore estuary position library liberation

Write the words in alphabetical order.

Comma says...

Learn these words for your sixth progress test.

thesaurus librarian

possessive

aimlessly

Write the Words

Cover each word and see if you can write it without looking.
Then check and write it again.

LOOK (THEN COVER)	WRITE	CHECK
object		
objection		
objectionable		
agree		
agreement		
agreeable		
disagreement		
disagreeable		
control		
controlling		
controlled		
controller		
council		
councillor		
cancel		
cancelled		
cancelling		
cancellation		
cruel		
cruelty		

Comma says...
Learn these words for your sixth progress test.

cancellation   cruelty

objectionable   councillor

Brodie's Brain Booster

Can you write a different word that can be made by adding a suffix to the word 'object'?

Use the words you have been practising to fill the gaps.

1 The perimeter of a circle is called the _____.

2 A county _____ came to visit our school.

3 Mum asked if the trousers were _____ if they didn't fit.

4 The Royal Society for the Prevention of _____ to Animals is known by the letters RSPCA.

5 I would like somebody to _____ me about which camera to buy.

6 I looked up some words in a _____.

7 The woman was _____ older than her husband.

8 A quadrilateral with opposite sides that are parallel is called a _____.

9 Because we couldn't go we had to arrange the _____ of our holiday.

10 Mum and I wandered _____ around the shops not knowing what to buy.

11 I don't like mushrooms but I find mushroom soup quite _____.

12 The boy's behaviour was really quite _____.

13 The _____ asked him to leave the library.

14 A triangle with equal sides is called an _____ triangle.

15 A triangle with two equal sides is called an _____ triangle.

16 Everybody who has a television has to have a television _____.

17 A long power cut was one _____ of the storm.

18 'This is my first _____ meal all day,' said Dad.

19 Some people are very good at sharing and others are very _____ about their belongings.

20 'If the noise doesn't go down I'm going to _____ silence in here,' said the teacher firmly.

Score _____ /20

38

Sort the Words

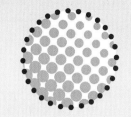

All the words on this page start with **con**.

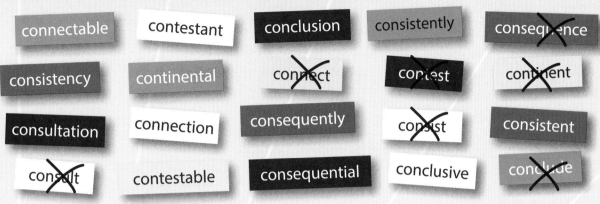

connectable   contestant   conclusion   consistently   ~~consequence~~

consistency   continental   ~~connect~~   ~~contest~~   ~~continent~~

consultation   connection   consequently   ~~consist~~   consistent

~~consult~~   contestable   consequential   conclusive   ~~conclude~~

Can you sort the words into groups?

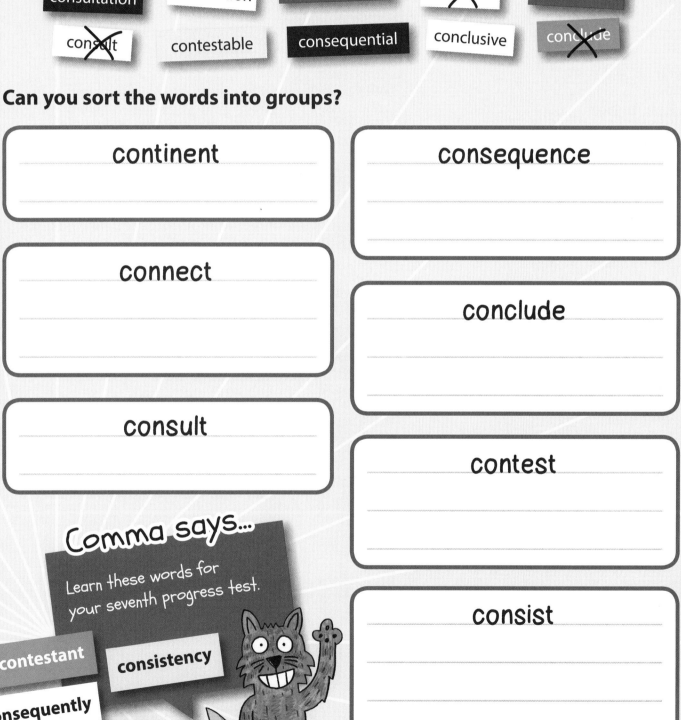

continent	consequence
connect	**conclude**
consult	**contest**
	consist

Comma says...

Learn these words for your seventh progress test.

contestant   consistency   consequently   connection

39

Practise the Words

Cover each word and see if you can write it without looking.
Then check and write it again.

LOOK (THEN COVER)	WRITE	CHECK
competition		
correspond		
criticise		
curiosity		
desperate		
determined		
develop		
disastrous		
environment		
equipped		

Choose words from above to complete the sentences below.

It's not nice to always _____ other people.

The new car is _____ with a satnav.

My mum was _____ to see the new baby.

I was delighted when I won the _____ .

Brodie's Brain Booster

Can you change the word 'compete' by adding a suffix to it?

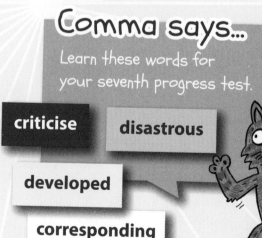

Comma says...

Learn these words for your seventh progress test.

criticise

disastrous

developed

corresponding

40

Pair the Words

Read the words below and then join each one to its pair. The first one has been done for you.

harass	interference
identity	marvellous
interfere	interruption
interrupt	physically
marvel	pronunciation
persuade	harassment
physical	recognition
profession	professional
pronounce	persuasion
recognise	identical

Comma says...

Learn these words for your seventh progress test.

identical   interruption

interference

pronunciation

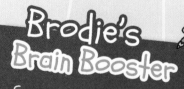

Brodie's Brain Booster

Can you add a prefix to the word 'professional' to make it into another word?

41

Alphabetical Order

Read the words below. Sometimes you need to look at the second, third or further letters of a word to work out alphabetical order.

signature primary stomach neighbour prejudice restaurant

sincerely nuisance opportunity sincere necessity secretary

relevant primarily recommend volunteer sacrifice voluntarily contemporary

shoulder boundary necessary soldier voluntary programme anniversary

Write the words in alphabetical order.

Comma says...

Learn these words for your seventh progress test.

restaurant programme

voluntarily necessary

42

Write the Words

Cover each word and see if you can write it without looking.
Then check and write it again.

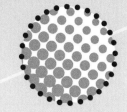

LOOK (THEN COVER)	WRITE	CHECK
encyclopedia		
pamphlet		
leaflet		
sphere		
spherical		
pharmacy		
level		
levelled		
levelling		
adventure		
adventurous		
encourage		
encouraging		
encouragingly		
encouragement		
flavour		
tourist		
tourism		
flourish		
nourish		

Comma says...

Learn these words for your seventh progress test.

encouragement

levelling tourism

spherical

Brodie's Brain Booster

Can you write the plural of 'pharmacy'?

Use the words you have been practising to fill the gaps.

1   My favourite television _____ is on tonight.

2   Only one _____ on the show is able to win a prize.

3   The builder was _____ the ground ready to dig the foundations.

4   Do you know the correct _____ of the word 'vase'?

5   'I think I've made a _____ mistake!' groaned Mum after she painted the bathroom dark green.

6   Halfway through my phone call the _____ was lost.

7   'I need to attach the wire to the _____ terminal,' said the electrician.

8   Sometimes it's _____ to write a word several times to learn to spell it.

9   The television signal was not clear because there was some _____.

10 The _____ of the dough was perfect for making the bread.

11 My teacher gives me lots of _____ with my work.

12 _____ is very important to some parts of the country.

13 Methods of transport have _____ considerably over the past century.

14 All the planets are _____ in shape.

15 Not all twins are _____.

16 Some twins do look very much alike so _____ many people find them difficult to tell apart.

17 Mum was surprised when I cut the grass _____.

18 I try not to _____ my friends.

19 'Please excuse the _____,' said the inspector when he came into our classroom.

20 We had a meal at a lovely _____.

Score /20

ANSWERS

Page 3 • Word Endings

assistance difference
importance absence
　　　　　　silence
　　　　　　independence
　　　　　　confidence
　　　　　　insistence
　　　　　　evidence

evidence
difference
assistant
confident
confidence
importance
distance

Brain Booster:
hindrance, nuisance, or any other words ending with 'ance'

Page 4 • Practise the Words

Words written as neatly as possible

United
monopolise
Union
Monopoly
unicycle
unity

Page 5 • Number Words

triplets quintet
tricycle quintuplet
triangular pentagon
　　　　　pentathlon

quartet
quadruped hexagonal
quadrilateral
　　　　　heptagon

　　　　　octagonal

　　　　　nonagon

　　　　　decagon
　　　　　decathlon

　　　　　century
　　　　　centenary
　　　　　centigrade

Page 6 • Sort the Words

Words starting with 'aqua':
aquarium
aquatic

Words starting with 'hydro' or 'hydra':
hydroelectric
hydrogen
hydraulic

Words starting with 'aero' or similar:
aerial
aeroplane
aerodynamic

Words starting with 'audio' or similar:
audible
audience
audio
audition
auditorium

Words starting with 'photo':
photographic
photocopier

Words starting with 'sub':
subject
submarine
submerge
subconscious
subheading

Page 7 • Practise the Words

Words written as neatly as possible

catalogue
guitars
guitarist
language

Brain Booster:
loyal (note that words such as soil, boil and toil are also acceptable)

Page 8 • Progress Test 1

1. evidence; 2. aeroplane
3. disguise; 4. hexagonal
5. guarantee; 6. importance
7. audition; 8. monologue
9. catalogue; 10. aquarium
11. assistance; 12. guidance
13. quadrilateral; 14. tricycle
15. unicycle; 16. reunion
17. submarine; 18. century
19. monorail; 20. independent

Page 9 • Sort the Words

expectant tolerant
expectantly tolerance
expectation toleration

hesitant substance
hesitation substantial
hesitantly substantially

　　　　　frequent
　　　　　frequency
　　　　　frequently

　　　　　confident
　　　　　confidence
　　　　　confidential

Page 10 • Practise the Words

Words written as neatly as possible

bruise
immediately
definite
government

Brain Booster:
lose, snooze, or any other appropriate rhyming word

Page 11 • Sort the Words

Words with 'qua':
quantity
quarrel
quarrelling
quarrelled
quality qualify
qualified
qualifying
qualification
disqualify

Words with 'que':
cheque oblique
antique
grotesque
equator
earthquake
queue conquer
sequence
mosque

Brain Booster:
sequential

Page 12 • Alphabetical Order

adorably	knight
applicable	obedience
applicably	obedient
application	plough
borough	practice
bough	practise
consumer	profit
container	prophet
continue	solemn
conversation	stationary
duet	stationery
duplicate	temperature
knife	thorough

Page 13 • Write the Words

Words written as neatly as possible

photograph autograph However supersonic microscope

Brain Booster:
forever, wherever, whenever, whatever, or any other appropriate word.

Page 14 • Progress Test 2

1. observation; 2. supersonic
3. accommodation
4. frequently; 5. stationery
6. microscopic; 7. immediately
8. stationary; 9. tolerant
10. quarrelling; 11. photographic
12. expectantly; 13. qualification
14. sequence; 15. practice
16. practise; 17. superior
18. quantity; 19. definite
20. government

Page 15 • Sort the Words

definite:
finite
define
definition
definitely
redefine
infinite
infinity
infinitely

preparing:
prepare
prepared
preparation
unprepared

excluding:
exclude
excluded
exclusion
exclusive
exclusively

Page 16 • Practise the Words

twelfth occur precarious achieve

Brain Booster:
rhythmic, rhythmical

Page 17 • Pair the Words

royal, royalty
actual, actually
general, generally
eventual, eventually
industry, industrial
rehearse, rehearsal
horizon, horizontal
vertical, vertically
original, originally
angel, angelic

Brain Booster:
cruelty, crueler, cruellest

Page 18 • Alphabetical Order

aggressive	meanwhile
although	portable
amateur	portfolio
ancient	prescription
apparent	primarily
conscience	primary
conscious	vegetable
controversy	vehicle
convenience	whatever
exaggerate	whenever
excellent	wherever
existence	whoever
explanation	yacht

Page 19 • Write the Words

Words written as neatly as possible

Brain Booster:
continent

Page 20 • Progress Test 3

1. secondary; 2. exclusively
3. available; 4. achievement
5. occupation; 6. aggressive
7. yacht; 8. infinity
9. conscience; 10. preparation
11. temporary; 12. explanation
13. variety; 14. rehearsal
15. previous; 16. Originally
17. definition; 18. sufficient
19. eventually; 20. Actually

Page 21 • Sort the Words

qualify:
qualified
qualifying
qualification
disqualify
disqualified
disqualifying
disqualification

respect:
respectful
disrespect
disrespectful

finance:
finances
financial
financier

commerce:
commercial
commercialise
commercialisation

Page 22 • Tricky Words

Words written as neatly as possible

deceive deceitful reception initial

Brain Booster:
cooperative, uncooperative, cooperatively, or any other appropriate word.

Page 23 • Pair the Words

island, islander
autumn, autumnal
consider, considerable
conscious, consciously
contest, contestant
continent, continental
consult, consultation
temporary, contemporary
adventure, adventurous

Page 24 • Alphabetical Order

angel	miserable
angle	obstinate
another	operation
anxious	opportunity
community	ordinary
competition	parliament
complicated	persuade
comprehension	physical
identity	prejudice
immediate	successful
medical	suggestion
medieval	surgery
mineral	surrender

Page 25 • Write the Words

Words written as neatly as possible

Brain Booster:
signature

Page 26 • Progress Test 4

1. prophecy; 2. adventurous
3. disqualified; 4. cancelled
5. ceiling; 6. immediate
7. considerable; 8. controlling
9. community; 10. islander
11. objection; 12. miserable
13. commercial; 14. financial
15. respectful; 16. Initially
17. ordinary; 18. consultation
19. cooperate; 20. receipt

Page 27 • Sort the Words

popular:
popularly
popularity
population

family:
familiar
familiarity
unfamiliar

regular:
regularly
irregular

peculiar:
peculiarly
peculiarity

particular:
particularly

sign:
signature
agriculture:
agricultural

Page 28 • Practise the Words

Words written as neatly as possible

principal
principles
deserts
dessert

Brain Booster:
deserted

Page 29 • Pair the Words

interfere, interference
interrupt, interruption
marvel, marvellous
mischief, mischievous
recognise, recognition
recommend, recommendation
secret, secretary
depend, dependable
sincere, sincerely

Brain Booster:
insincere, or any other
appropriate word

Page 30 • Alphabetical Order

atmosphere	phenomenon
atmospheric	privilege
attraction	profession
attractive	programme
boarder	pronunciation
border	shattered
bought	shoulder
brought	soldier
conclusion	stomach
consequence	tornado
considerable	tortuous
consistent	tournament
phenomenal	tremendous

Page 31 • Write the Words

Words written as neatly as possible

Brain Booster:
palace, or any other appropriate
rhyming word

Page 32 • Progress Test 5

1. agricultural; 2. atmosphere
3. innocently; 4. mischievous
5. delightful; 6. compliment
7. dessert; 8. delicious
9. tournament; 10. precious
11. interruption; 12. popularity
13. unfamiliar; 14. particularly
15. recommendation
16. privilege; 17. boarder
18. principal; 19. draught
20. individually

Page 33 • Sort the Words

consider:
considerable
considerably
consideration

tolerate:
toleration
tolerable
tolerably

force:
forcible
enforce
enforcement

change:
changeable
changeability
changeless
changelessness
exchange
exchangeable
exchangeability

Page 34 • Practise the Words

Words written as neatly as possible

advice
advise
devise
licence

Brain Booster:
effective, effectual, or any other appropriate word

Page 35 • Tricky Mathematical Words

Words written as neatly as possible

dodecahedron
cylindrical
equilateral
cylinder
circumference

Brain Booster:
cuboid

Page 36 • Alphabetical Order

ailment
aimlessly
airbrush
aisle
especially
essential
estimation
estuary
liberation
librarian
library
litter
medallion
medieval
mineral
ministry
parliament
particular
position
positively
possessive
possibly
therapist
therapy
therefore
thesaurus

Page 37 • Write the Words

Words written as neatly as possible

Brain Booster:
objecting, objected, or any other appropriate word

Page 38 • Progress Test 6

1. circumference; 2. councillor
3. exchangeable; 4. Cruelty
5. advise; 6. thesaurus
7. considerably; 8. parallelogram
9. cancellation; 10. aimlessly
11. tolerable; 12. objectionable
13. librarian; 14. equilateral
15. isosceles; 16. licence
17. effect; 18. decent
19. possessive; 20. enforce

Page 39 • Sort the Words

continent:
continental

connect:
connectable
connection

consult:
consultation

consequence:
consequential
consequently

conclude:
conclusion
conclusive

contest:
contestant
contestable

consist:
consistent
consistently
consistency

Page 40 • Practise the Words

Words written as neatly as possible

criticise
equipped
desperate
competition

Brain Booster:
competing, competed, competitor, or any other appropriate word

Well done!

Page 41 • Pair the Words

harass, harassment
identity, identical
interfere, interference
interrupt, interruption
marvel, marvellous
persuade, persuasion
physical, physically
profession, professional
pronounce, pronunciation
recognise, recognition

Brain Booster:
unprofessional

Page 42 • Alphabetical Order

anniversary
boundary
contemporary
necessary
necessity
neighbour
nuisance
opportunity
prejudice
primarily
primary
programme
recommend
relevant
restaurant
sacrifice
secretary
shoulder
signature
sincere
sincerely
soldier
stomach
voluntarily
voluntary
volunteer

Page 43 • Write the Words

Words written as neatly as possible

Brain Booster:
pharmacies

Page 44 • Progress Test 7

1. programme; 2. contestant
3. levelling; 4. pronunciation
5. disastrous; 6. connection
7. corresponding; 8. necessary
9. interference; 10. consistency
11. encouragement
12. tourism; 13. developed
14. spherical; 15. identical
16. consequently; 17. voluntarily
18. criticise; 19. interruption
20. restaurant